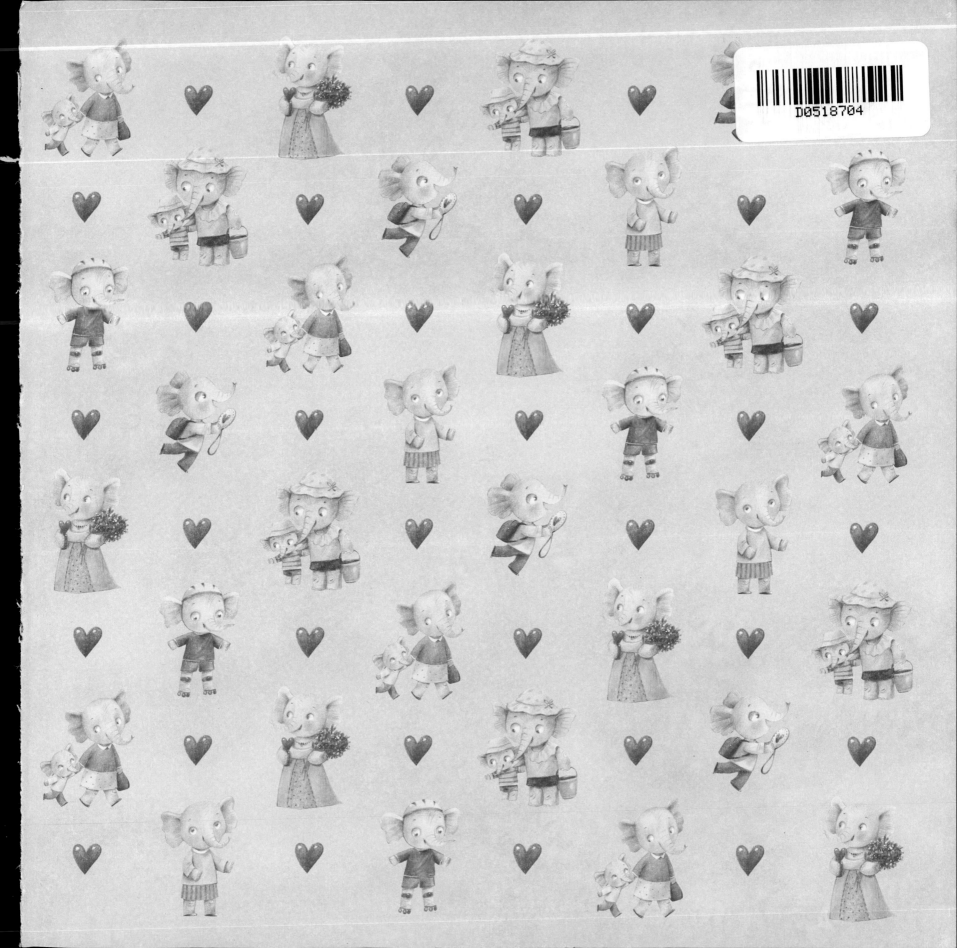

This igloo book belongs to:

....

igloobooks

Published in 2020
by Igloo Books Ltd
Cottage Farm
Sywell
NN6 0BJ
www.igloobooks.com

Copyright © 2018 Igloo Books Ltd
Igloo Books is an imprint of Bonnier Books UK

0220 001
2 4 6 8 10 9 7 5 3 1
ISBN 978-1-83903-860-0

Written by Stephanie Moss
Illustrated by Ela Jarzabek

Designed by Katie Messenger
Edited by Natalia Boileau

Printed and manufactured in China

The
Greatest
Mummy of All

igloobooks

You're the **greatest** mummy. I love you more with every day.
There are lots of reasons why, almost too many to say.

You're always there to lean on, with a **loving** hand to hold.

If there was a Mummy Medal, I know yours would be **gold**.

No matter where we are, you always make it feel like **home**.
I love you because I know I'll never be alone.

I'm sure no one has as much **fun** as us when we're together.

You know just how to make me **laugh**, no matter what the weather.

You're the **kindest** mummy and do you know how it shows?

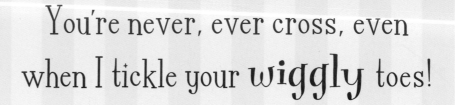

You're never, ever cross, even
when I tickle your **wiggly** toes!

When I'm feeling nervous, a bit lonely or just shy...

... you're right there behind me, saying,
"It's okay to try."

You're not just my mummy, you're my **best** friend, as well.

You know all my **special** secrets. There's no one else I'd tell.

No one in the world makes a bad day **better** quite like you.

One **kiss** and a cuddle makes
everything as good as new.

You could be almost **perfect**. At least that's how it seems.
You deserve a Best Mummy Award, one that glitters and gleams.

When you sing me a lullaby, I know everything's alright.
You're the one I **dream** of when I fall asleep at night.

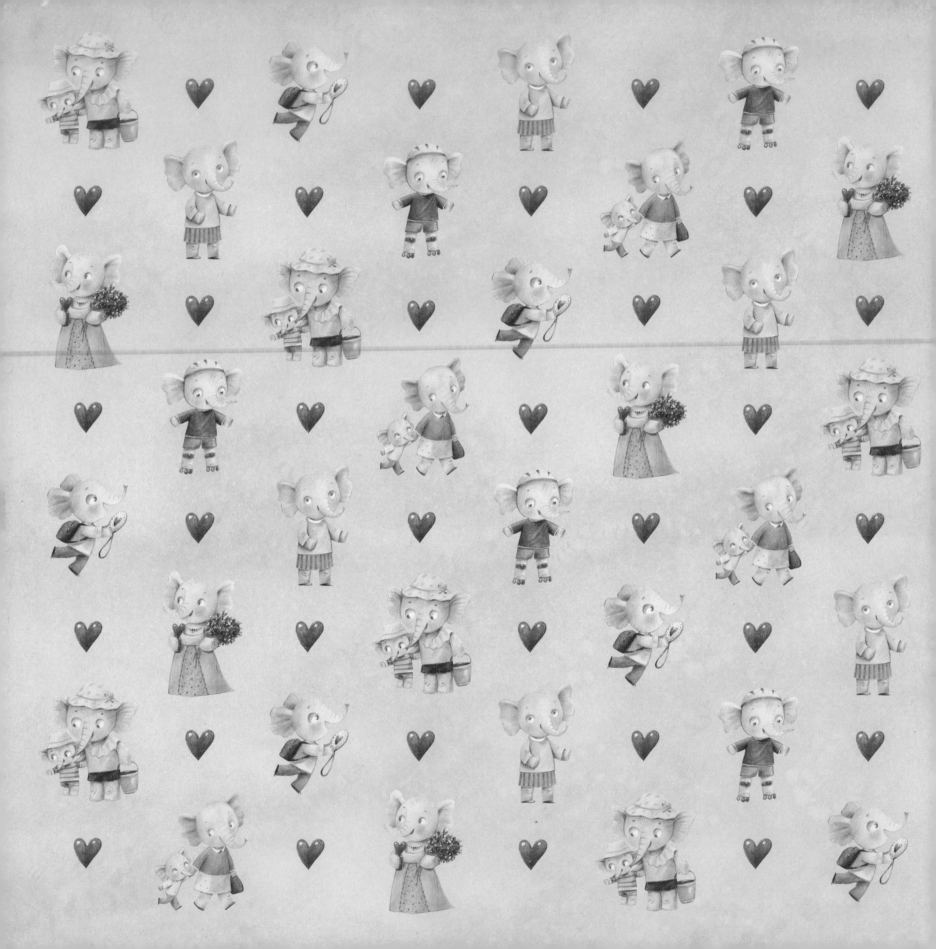